The Afternoon Pianist

Wise Publications
part of The Music Sales Group

London/New York/Sydney/Paris/Copenhagen/Madrid/Tokyo

Published by
Wise Publications
8/9 Frith Street, London W1D 3JB, England.

Exclusive distributors:
Music Sales Limited
Distribution Centre, Newmarket Road,
Bury St Edmunds, Suffolk IP33 3YB, England.
Music Sales Pty Limited
120 Rothschild Avenue, Rosebery, NSW 2018, Australia.

Order No. AM84112
ISBN 0-7119-2583-6
This book © Copyright 2003 by Wise Publications

Music arranged by Derek Jones & Jerry Lanning.
Music processed by Enigma Music Production Services.
Compiled, written & edited by Sarah Holcroft.
Cover photograph courtesy of Images Colour Library.

Printed in the United Kingdom by
Thanet Press Limited, Margate, Kent.

www.musicsales.com

Foreword

The Afternoon Pianist has been specially designed to cater for the less experienced adult learner.

This larger-print compilation features a mixture of traditional carols as well as some of the most popular Christmas hits, by artists such as Perry Como, John Lennon and George Michael.

The titles have been arranged in order of difficulty, allowing you to work your way through the collection learning new techniques, keys and time signatures.

A glossary has been provided as a quick reference to any unknown musical terms and symbols.

Each piece is accompanied by a short tutorial which offers guidance on how to tackle the more difficult aspects of the music. Fingerings and chord diagrams are provided throughout.

Learning a piece of music takes time and dedication. We hope that our tips will help to make learning easier, so that you can really enjoy playing the music in this collection.

Silent Night

Words by Joseph Mohr
Music by Franz Gruber

Coventry Carol

Traditional

Watch out for accidentals in this piece.
The key is A minor, so we expect some accidental G♯s to appear (e.g. R.H. Bar 1).
However, there are also some G♮s which are used occasionally, giving the piece a modal feel.

Use these diagrams as a guide to help you find the chords in bar 20:

KEY

A minor

G♯, G♮

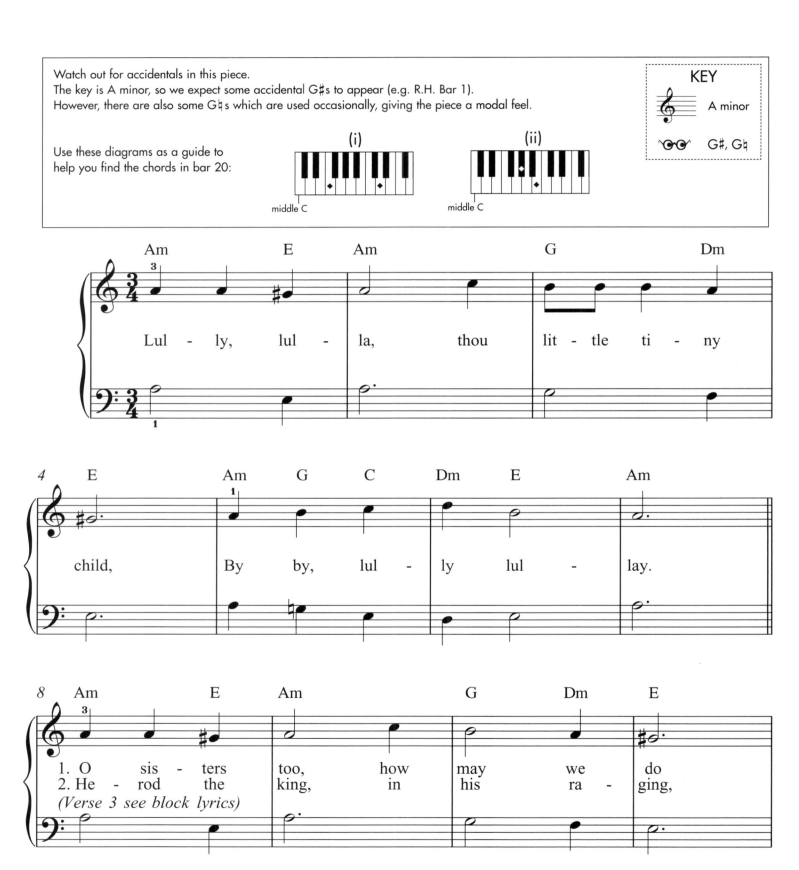

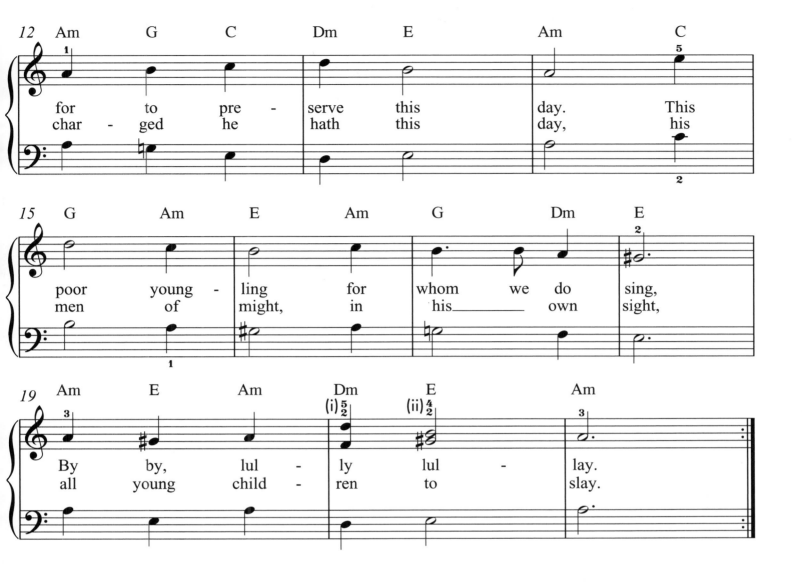

Verse 3:
That woe is me, poor child for thee!
And ever morn and day,
For thy parting neither say nor sing
By by, lully lullay!

O Come All Ye Faithful

Original Words & Music by John Francis Wade
English Words by Frederick Oakeley

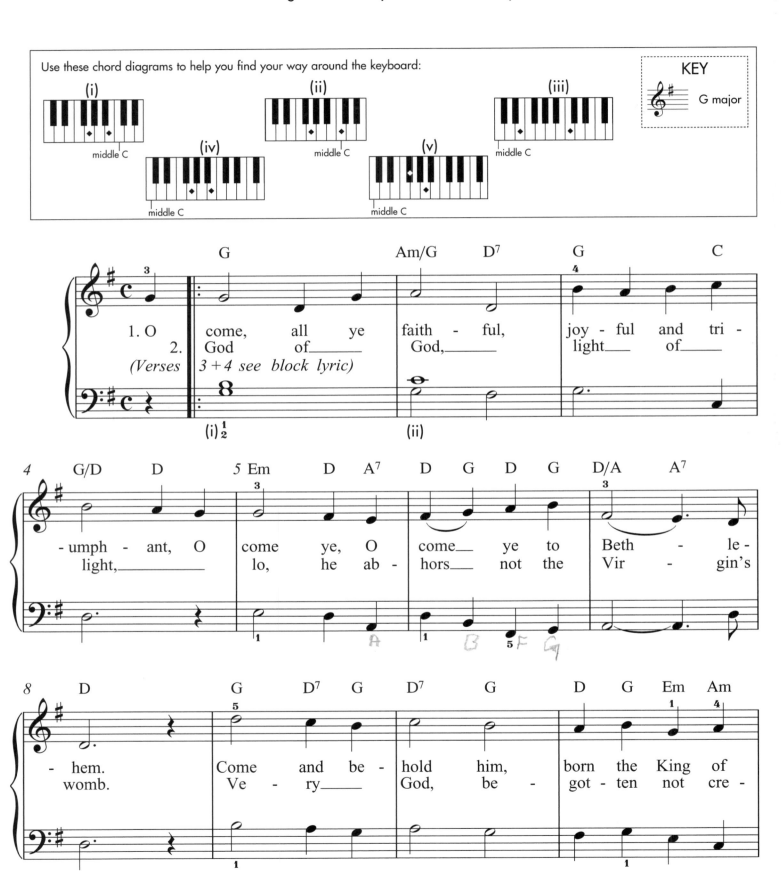

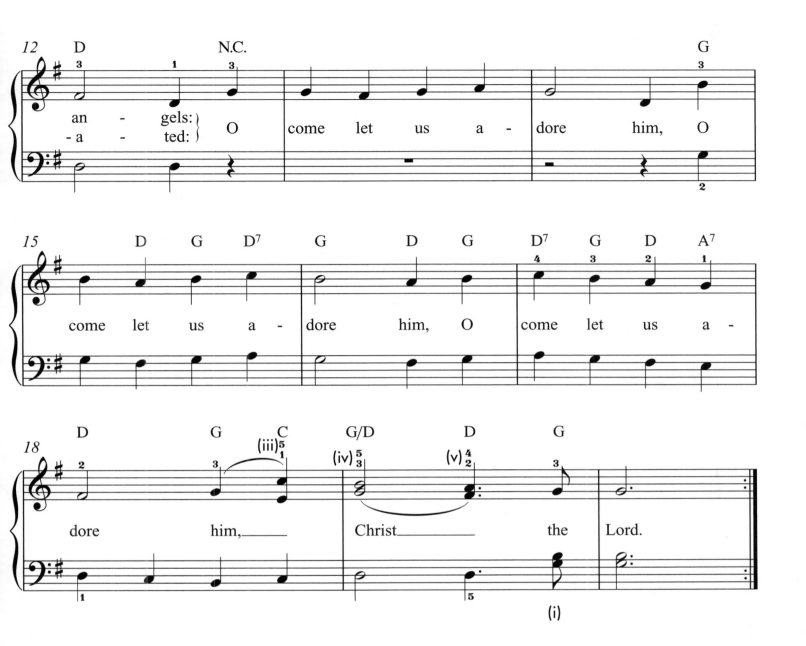

Verse 3:
Sing choirs of angels,
Sing in exultation,
Sing, all ye citizens of heav'n above.
Glory to God in the highest:

O come let us etc.

Verse 4:
Yea, Lord, we greet thee
Born this happy morning
Jesu, to thee be glory giv'n.
Word of the Father, now in flesh appearing:

O come let us etc.

Angels From The Realms Of Glory

Traditional
Words by James Montgomery

Bars 5-8 are an exact repeat of bars 1-4.
Bars 9-14 are almost identical to bars 15-20.

R.H. The notes of bar 9 are repeated in bar 10 one tone lower than previously,
and then again in bar 11, a tone lower than in bar 10.
This is known as a descending *sequence*:

KEY

G major

F♮

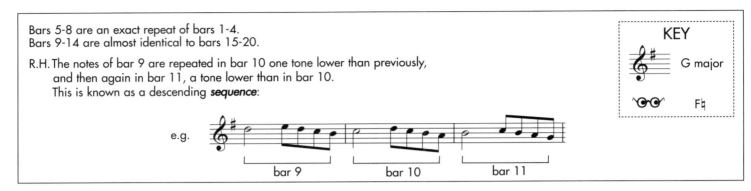

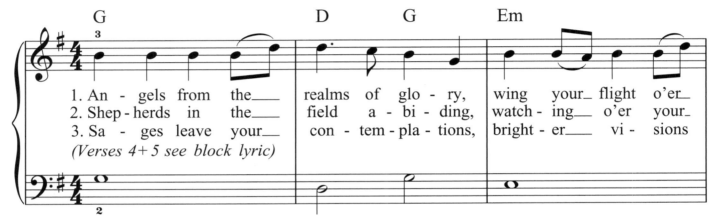

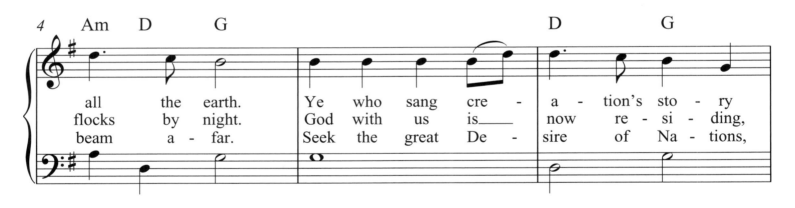

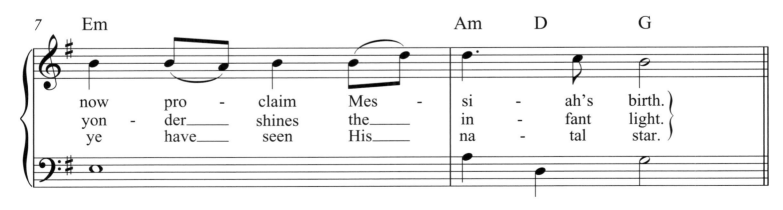

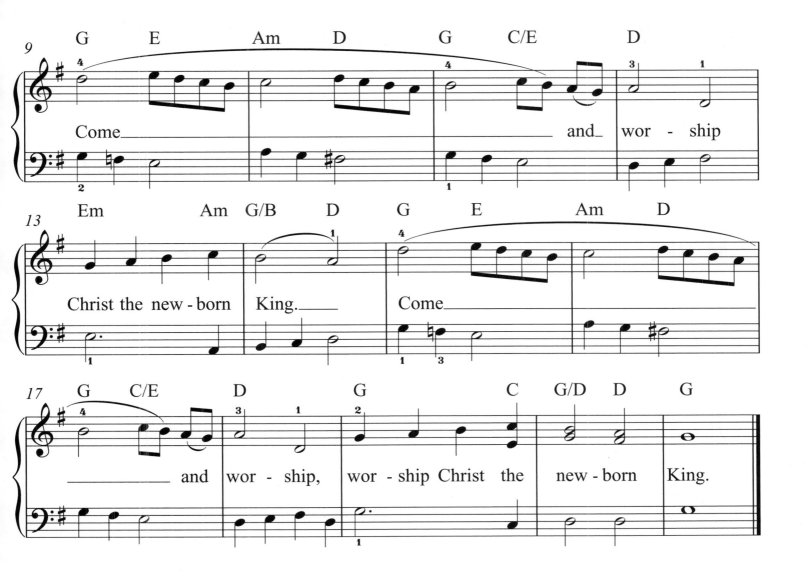

Verse 4:
Saints before the alter bending,
Watching long in hope and fear,
Suddenly the Lord, descending,
In his temple shall appear.

Come etc.

Verse 5:
Though an infant now we view him,
He shall fill his father's throne,
Gather all the nations to him;
Ev'ry knee shall then bow down.

Come etc.

The First Nowell

Traditional

Bars 1-8 are repeated exactly in bars 9-16.

Use these diagrams to help you with some of the more tricky R.H. chords in bars 17 to the end:

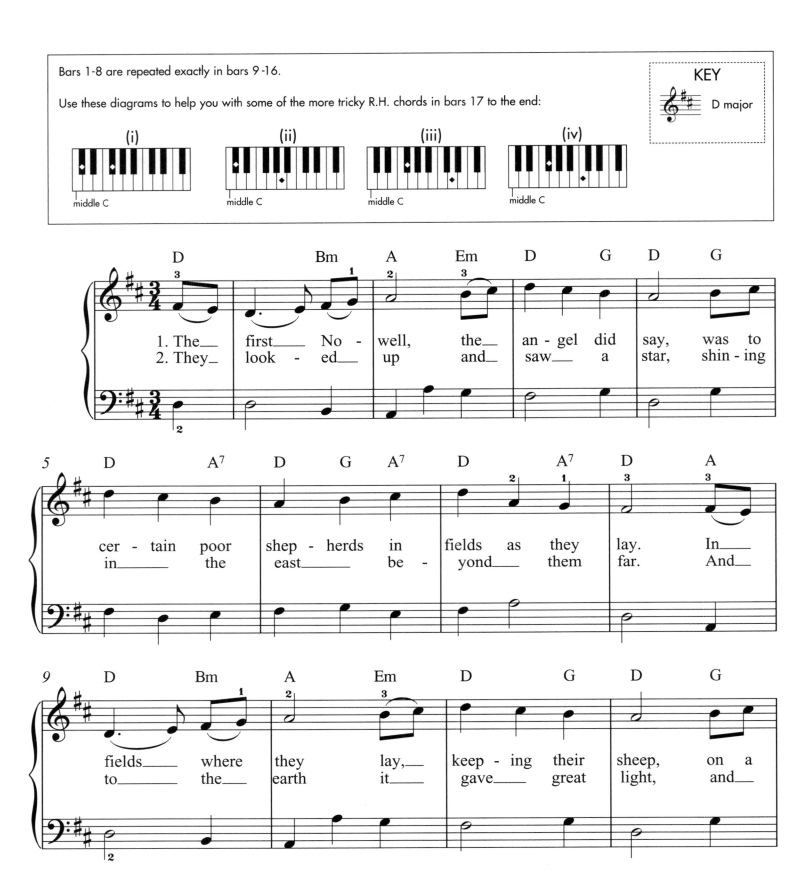

Verse 3:
And by the light of that same star,
Three wise men came from country far;
To seek for a king was their intent,
And to follow the star wherever it went.

Nowell etc.

Verse 4:
This star drew nigh to the north-west,
O'er Bethlehem it took its rest,
And there it did both stop and stay
Right over the place where Jesus lay.

Nowell etc.

We Three Kings

Words & Music by John Henry Hopkins

The time signature $\frac{3}{8}$ should be treated in exactly the same way as $\frac{3}{4}$, i.e. 3 beats in a bar.
The **8** indicates that the beats are *quavers* rather than *crotchets*,
so, the pace should be slightly quicker in this piece.

R.H. Often the thumb acts as an anchor,
i.e. it is held down while the tune is played above.

If you find it easier, practise the tune alone and add
the second voice when you feel more confident:

e.g. bars 12 & 13:

tune (Voice 1)

Voice 2

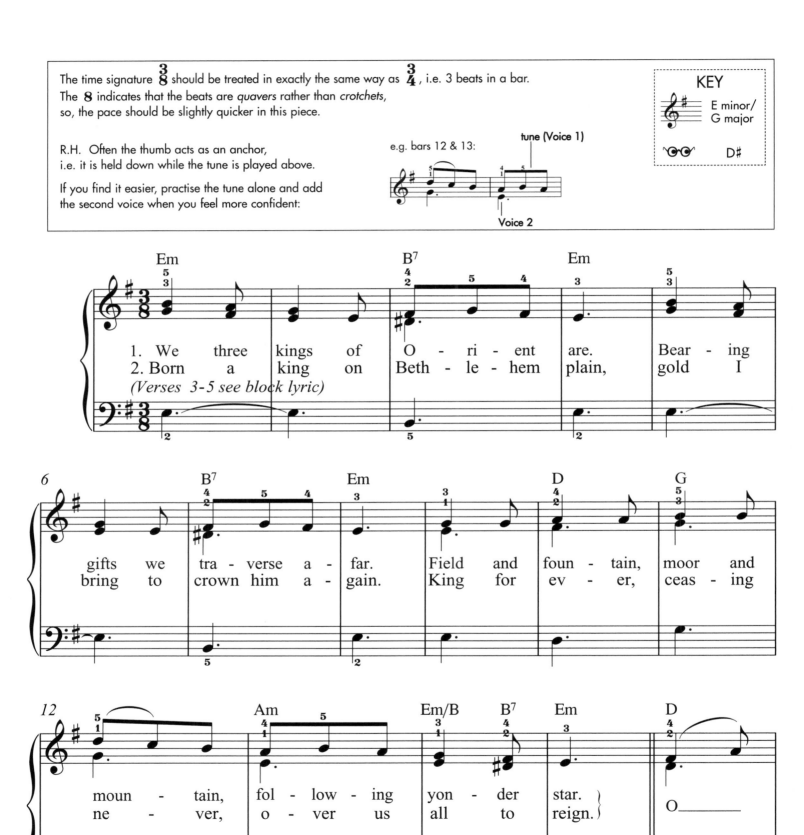

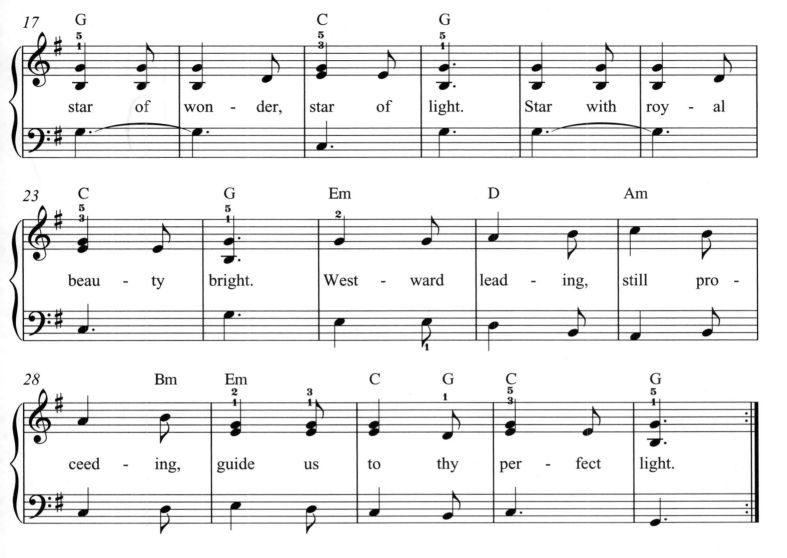

Verse 3:
Frankincense to offer have I,
Incense owns a Deity nigh.
Prayer and praising, gladly raising
Worship him, God most high!

O star etc.

Verse 4:
Myrrh is mine, its bitter perfume
Breathes a life of gathering gloom
Sorrowing, sighing, bleeding, dying;
Sealed in a stone-cold tomb.

O star etc.

Verse 5:
Glorious now behold him arise,
King and God and sacrifice;
Alleluia, alleluia,
Earth to heav'n replies.

O star etc.

Lonely This Christmas

Words & Music by Mike Chapman & Nicky Chinn

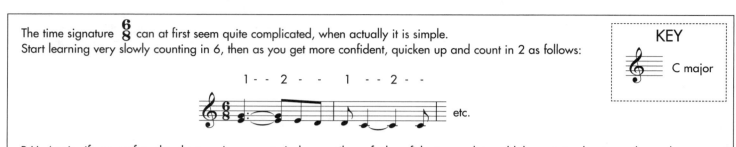

The time signature **6/8** can at first seem quite complicated, when actually it is simple.
Start learning very slowly counting in 6, then as you get more confident, quicken up and count in 2 as follows:

KEY

C major

R.H. Again, if you prefer, play the tune (upper notes) alone until you feel confident enough to add the sustained notes underneath.

O Come, O Come, Emmanuel

Traditional
English Words by John Neale

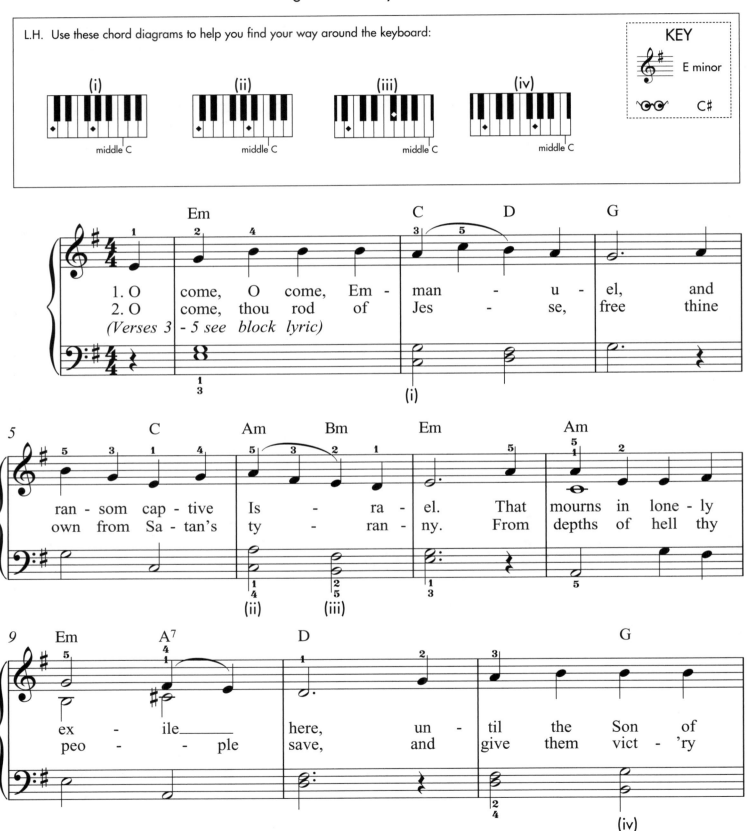

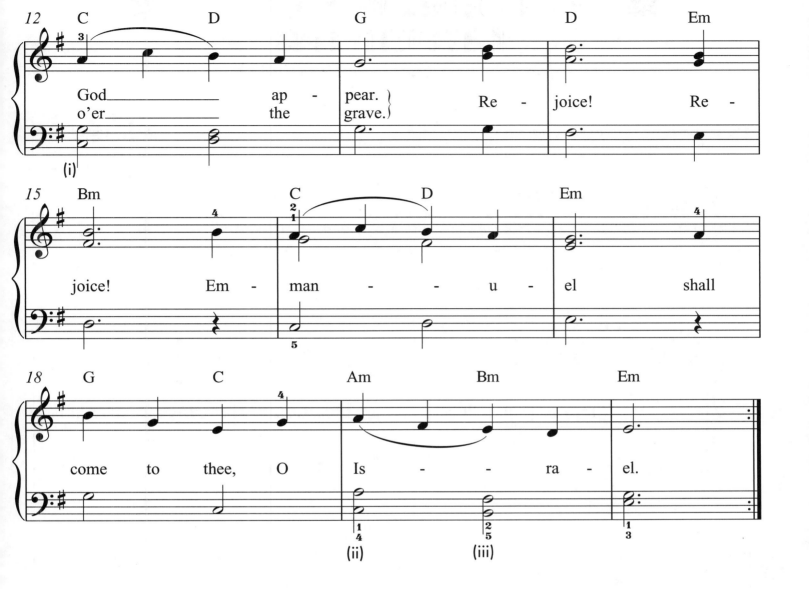

Verse 3:
O come, thou dayspring, come and cheer
Our spirits by thine advent here;
Disperse the gloomy clouds of night,
And death's dark shadows put to flight.

Verse 4:
O come, thou key of David, come
And open wide our heav'nly home.
Make safe the way that leads on high
And close the path to misery.

Verse 5:
O come, o come thou Lord of might,
Who to thy tribes on Sinai's height
In ancient times didst give the Law
In cloud and majesty and awe.

I Believe In Father Christmas

Words & Music by Greg Lake & Peter Sinfield

The rhythm in both hands looks more complicated than it actually is.
Imagine two straight crotchets and a minim, with the first crotchet held down:

Use the steady left hand beats as a constant above which you can fit in the syncopated right hand notes.

Bars 16-32: both hands are in *unison,* i.e. they play exactly the same notes an octave apart.
Pay close attention to the fingerings suggested and practise both hands separately until you feel confident enough to put them together.

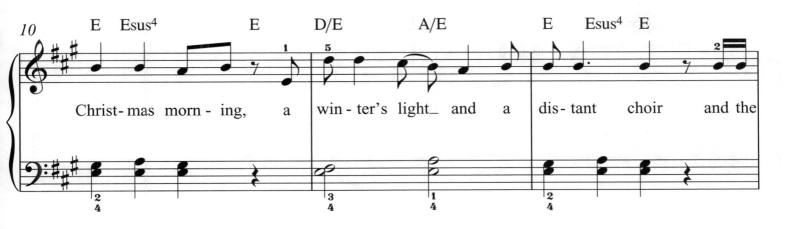

Christ-mas morn-ing, a win-ter's light and a dis-tant choir and the

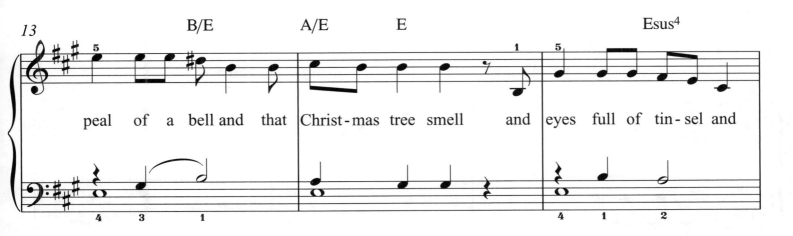

peal of a bell and that Christ-mas tree smell and eyes full of tin-sel and

To ⊕ Coda

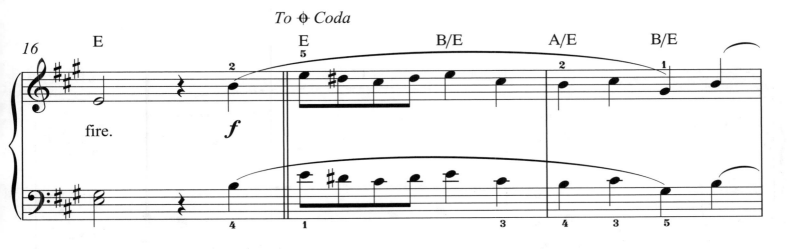

fire. *f*

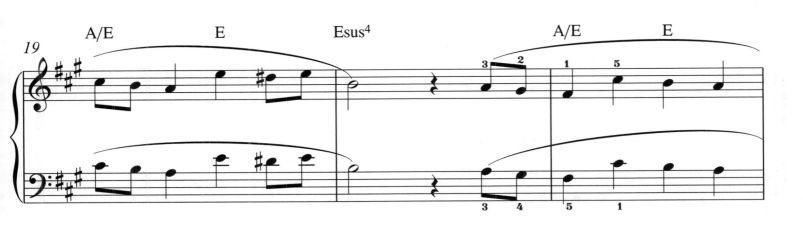

23

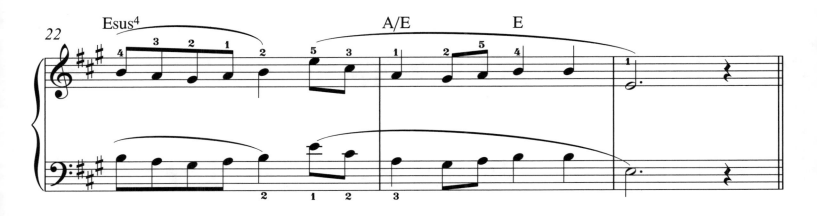

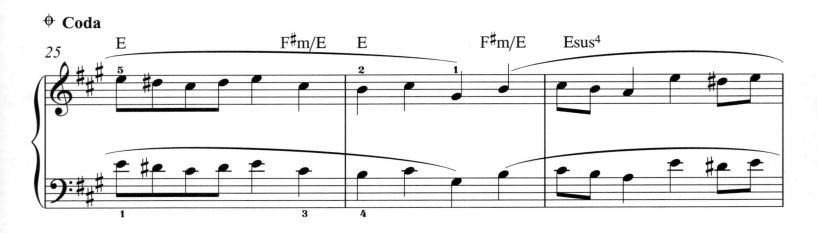

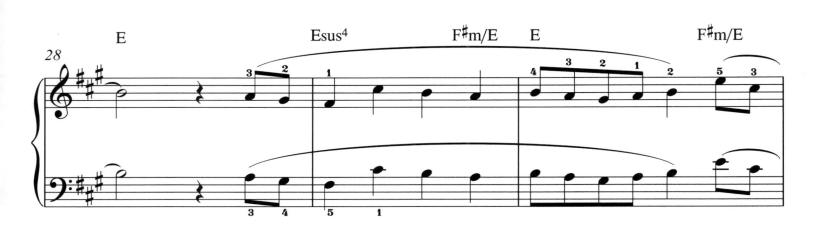

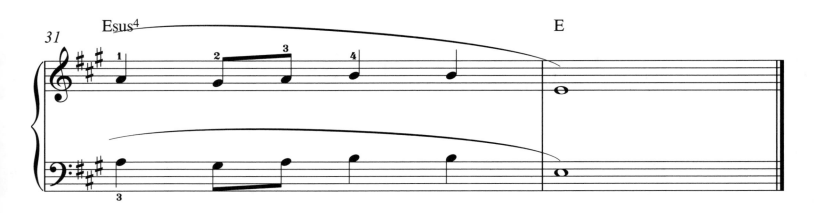

Last Christmas

Words & Music by George Michael

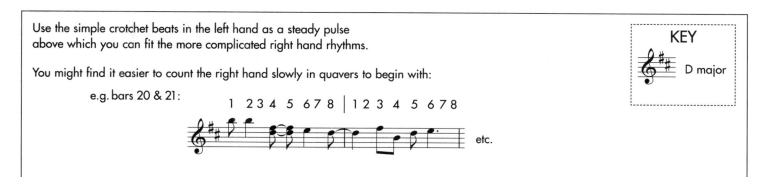

With bounce

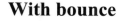

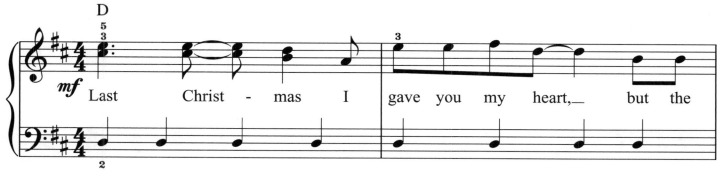

25

Once bit-ten and twice shy,____ I keep my dis-tance but

you still catch__ my eye.__ Tell me ba-by, do you re-cog-nise me?

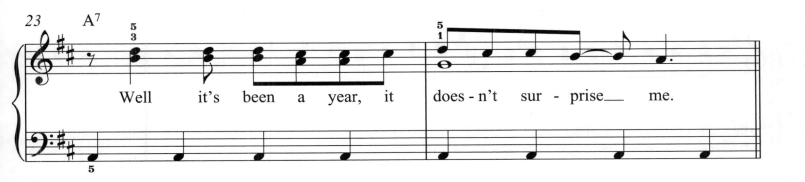

Well it's been a year, it does-n't sur-prise___ me.

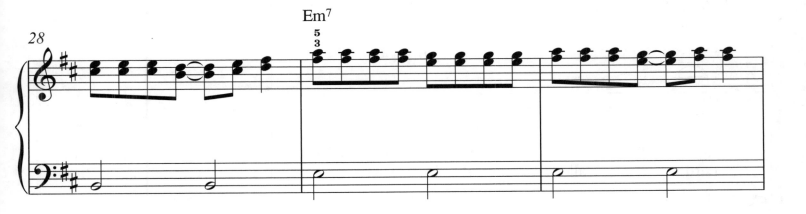

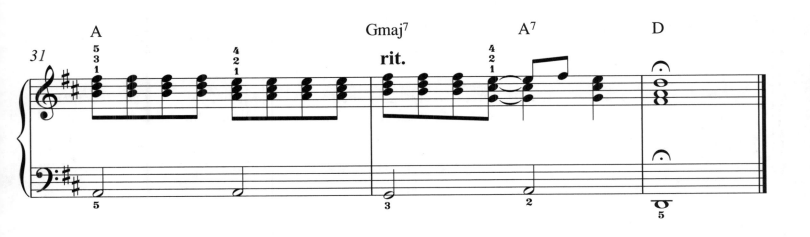

Once In Royal David's City

Words by Cecil Alexander
Music by Henry Gauntlett

This piece is made up of three 4-bar phrases, two of which are almost identical.
Practise each phrase independently, and then put the three together.

♪ Phrase 1: Bars 1-4
♪ Phrase 2: Bars 5-8 (a repeat of bars 1-4 with a slight change to the harmony in bar 6)
♪ Phrase 3: Bars 9-2

Try varying the dynamics for each verse you play.
Start *mp* in verse 1, and finish *ff* in verse 5.

KEY

G major

C#

moth - er mild,   Je - sus   Christ   her | lit - tle____ child.
mean   and   low - ly | lived   on   earth   a | Sa - viour__ holy.

Verse 3:
And through all his wondrous childhood
Day by day like us he grew;
He was little, weak and helpless,
Tears and smiles like us he knew;
And he feeleth for our sadness,
And he shareth in our gladness.

Verse 4:
Still among the poor and lowly
Hope in Christ is brought to birth,
With the promise of salvation
For the nations of the earth;
Still in him our life is found
And our hope of heav'n is crowned.

Verse 5:
And our eyes at last shall see him
Through his own redeeming love,
For that child so dear and gentle
Is our Lord in heav'n above;
And he leads his children on
To the place where he is gone.

Away In A Manger

Words: Traditional
Music by William Kirkpatrick

Verse 2: The cattle are lowing, the baby awakes,
But little Lord Jesus no crying he makes.
I love thee, Lord Jesus! Look down from the sky,
And stay by my side until morning is nigh.

Verse 3: Be near me, Lord Jesus; I ask Thee to stay
Close by me for ever, and love me, I pray.
Bless all the dear children in thy tender care,
And fit us for heaven, to live with Thee there.

Wonderful Christmastime

Words & Music by Paul McCartney

The middle section of this piece (bars 17-32) contains a series of consecutive 6ths.

The exercise below will help to accustom the right hand with the sixth position.
Practise over and over using the fingerings provided.
Bars 17-32 will appear a lot easier after mastering this exercise.

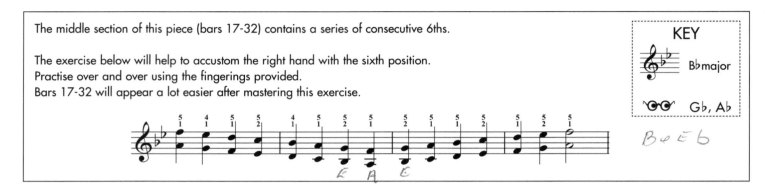

Brightly

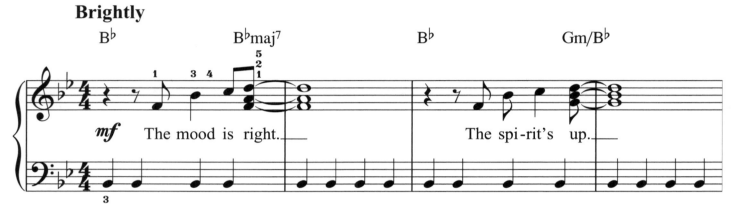

The mood is right. — The spi-rit's up. —

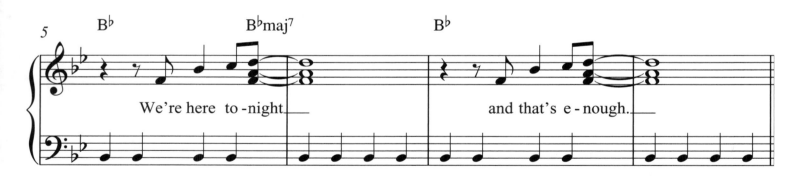

We're here to-night. — and that's e-nough. —

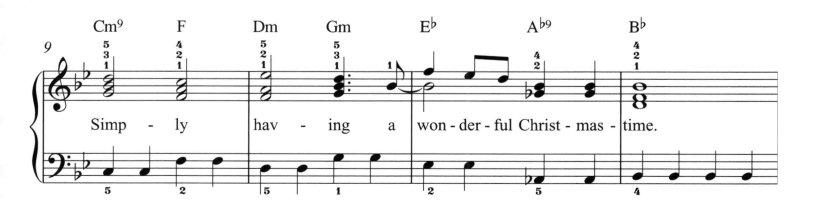

Simp - ly hav - ing a won - der - ful Christ - mas - time.

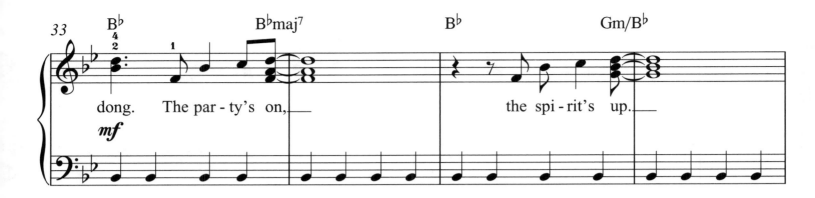

dong. The par-ty's on,⎯⎯⎯   the spi-rit's up.⎯⎯⎯

mf

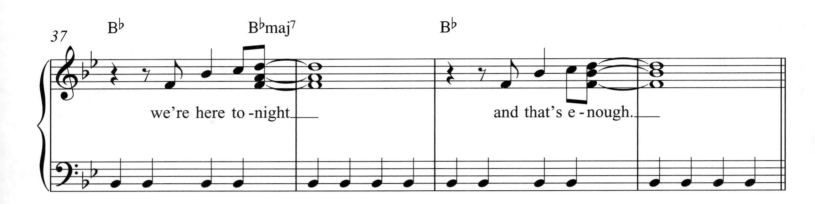

we're here to-night⎯⎯⎯   and that's e-nough.⎯⎯⎯

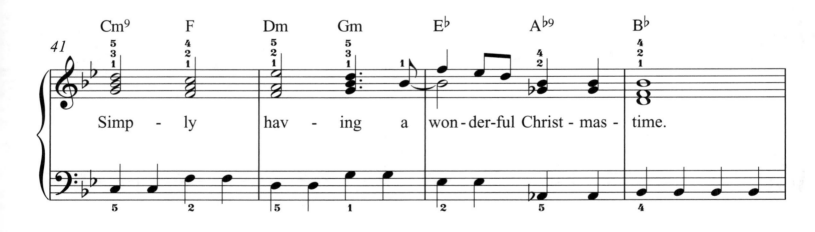

Simp — ly   hav — ing   a   won-der-ful Christ-mas - time.

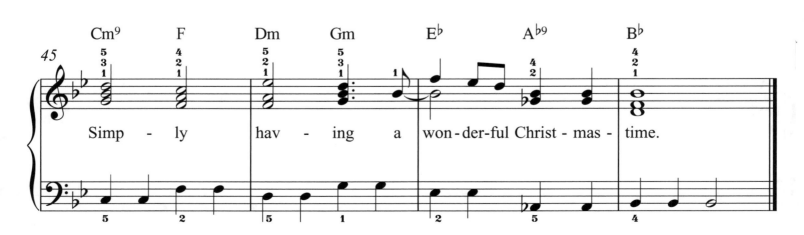

Simp — ly   hav — ing   a   won-der-ful Christ-mas - time.

Mistletoe And Wine

Words by Leslie Stewart & Jeremy Paul
Music by Keith Strachan

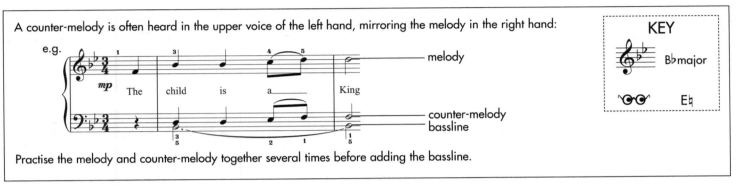

I Wish It Could Be Christmas Every Day

Words & Music by Roy Wood

There are some tricky left hand leaps throughout this piece. Here are three tips which should make these easier:

1) Look Ahead
Try glancing a couple of bars ahead while you are playing. This will help you to spot difficult jumps before they arrive.

2) Get Into Position
Rests provide a great opportunity for you to move your hand into the correct position in advance of playing the next note.

3) Use Fingerings
All fingering suggestions have been provided in order to make things as easy on your hands as possible. Follow them.

© Copyright 1973 Roy Wood.
All Rights Reserved. International Copyright Secured.

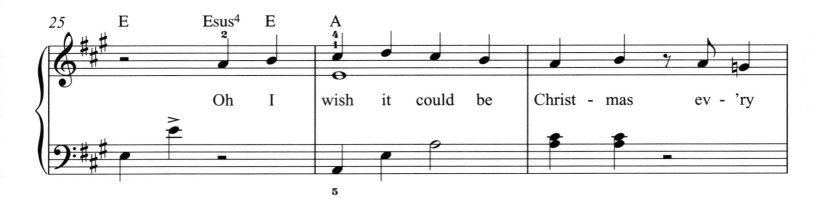

Oh I wish it could be Christ - mas ev - 'ry

day.___ So let the bells ring out for

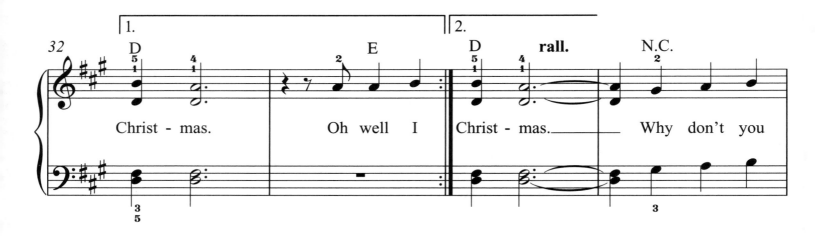

1.

Christ - mas. Oh well I

2. **rall.**

Christ - mas.___ Why don't you

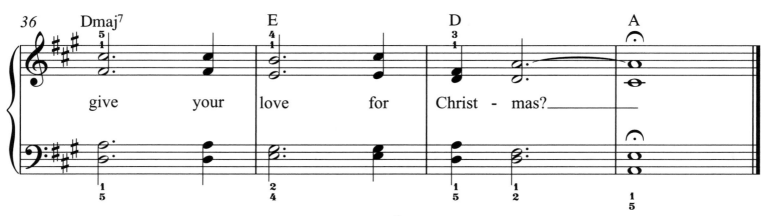

give your love for Christ - mas?___

Happy Xmas (War Is Over)

Words & Music by John Lennon & Yoko Ono

Before you start to play, notice that the first 8 bars in the left hand are identical to those of the chorus:

e.g. bars 2 & 3  etc.

Indeed, the left hand repeats this 'War is over' melody throughout the piece, first in D major (bars 1-9), next in G major (bars 10-17), then in C major (bars 18-27) and finally back in D major (bars 28-35).

Breaking it into four-bar sections, learn the left hand thoroughly before you attempt to add the right hand.

KEY

D major

Ch, D#

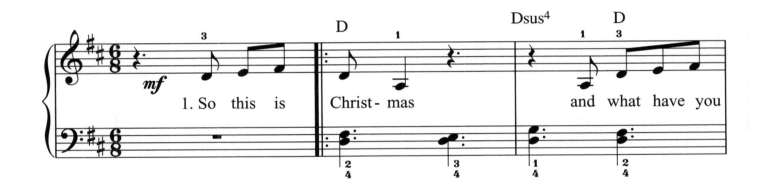

1. So this is Christ - mas and what have you

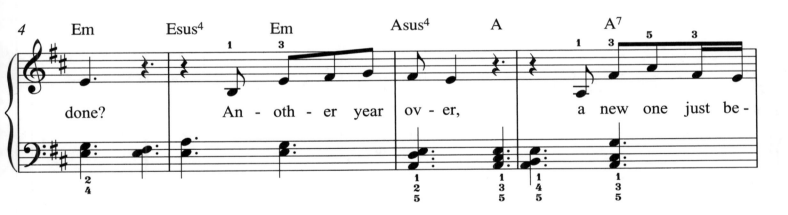

done? An - oth - er year ov - er, a new one just be -

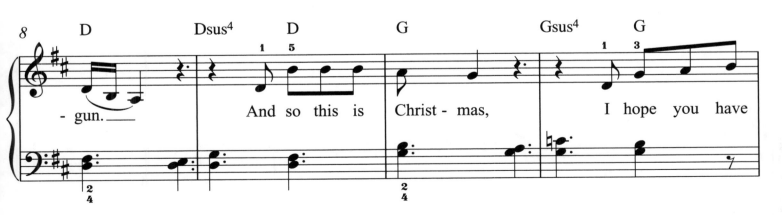

- gun.___ And so this is Christ - mas, I hope you have

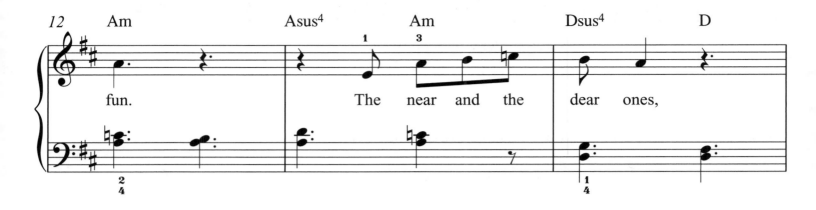

12 Am   Asus⁴   Am   Dsus⁴   D

fun.   The near and the   dear ones,

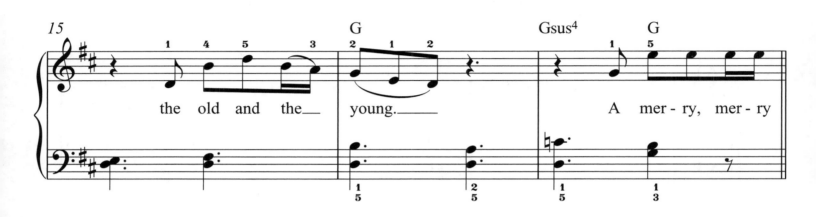

15   G   Gsus⁴   G

the old and the___ young._____   A mer - ry, mer - ry

18 C   D

Christ - mas_____   and a hap - py New Year,

21   Am   C

let's hope it's a   good one,_____   with - out an - y

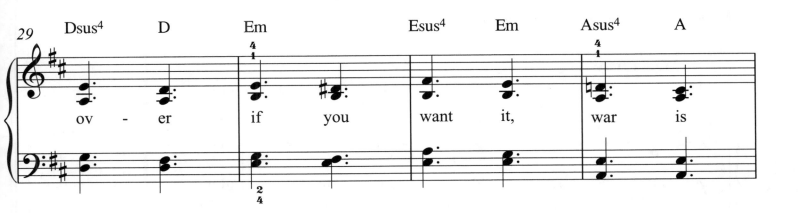

Verse 2: And so this is Christmas, for weak and for strong,
The rich and the poor ones; the road is so long.
And so, happy Christmas, for black and for white,
For the yellow and red ones; let's stop all the fights.
A merry, merry Christmas
And a happy New Year,
Let's hope it's a good one,
Without any fear.

War is over if you want it,
War is over now.

Hark! The Herald Angels Sing

Music by Felix Mendelssohn
Words by Charles Wesley

One of the difficulties of learning hymns is that there is a lot of activity going on in both hands at the same time. To overcome this problem, learn this piece in four stages:

1) Familiarise yourself with the tune alone (voice 1) in the right hand.

2) Now try adding the bassline (voice 4) in the left hand.

3) Now play the tune, bassline and add voice 2 in the right hand.

4) Finally, when you're feeling confident enough, add voice 3 in the left hand.

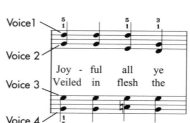

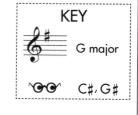

Verse 3:
Hail, the heav'n-born Prince of Peace!
Hail, the Sun of Righteousness!
Light and life to all he brings
Ris'n with healing in his wings.
Mild he lays his glory by,
Born that man no more may die,
Born to raise his sons to earth,
Born to give them second birth:

45

O Little Town Of Bethlehem

Words by Phillips Brooks
Music by Lewis Redner

Bars 5-8 are an exact repeat of bars 1-4.
Bars 12-16 are also virtually identical but watch out for the slight harmony change in bar 14.

Use these chord diagrams as a guide to help you find your way around the keyboard:

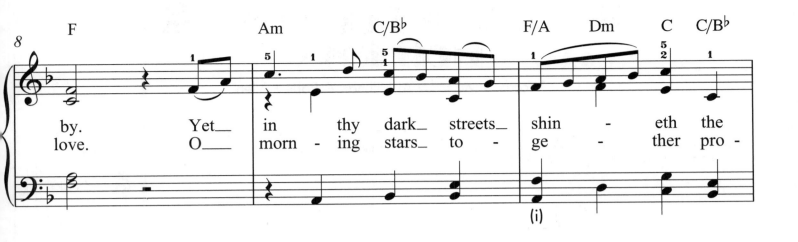

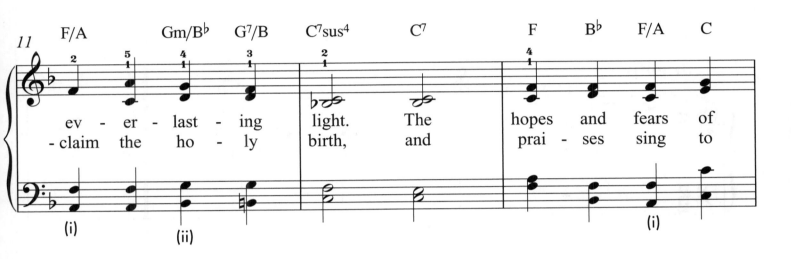

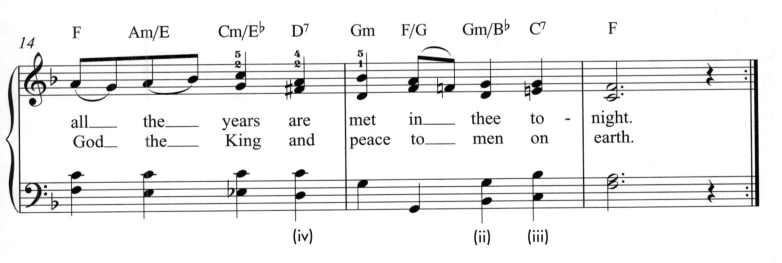

Verse 3:
How silently, how silently
The wondrous gift is giv'n!
So God imparts to human hearts
The blessings of his heav'n.
No ear may hear his coming
But in this world of sin,
Where meek souls will receive him, still
The dear Christ enters in.

Verse 4:
O holy child of Bethlehem
Descend to us, we pray;
Cast out our sin, and enter in,
Be born in us today.
We hear the Christmas angels
The great glad tidings tell:
O come to us, abide with us,
Our Lord Emmanuel.

Home For The Holidays

Words & Music by Al Stillman & Robert Allen

Frosty The Snowman

Words & Music by Steve Nelson & Jack Rollins

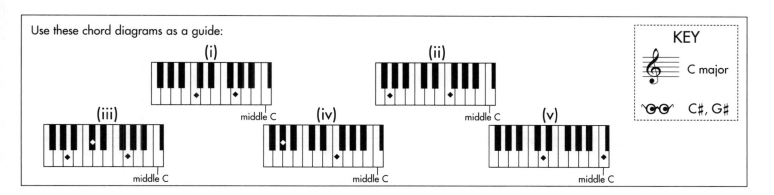

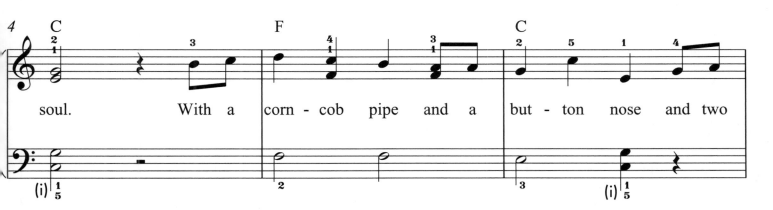

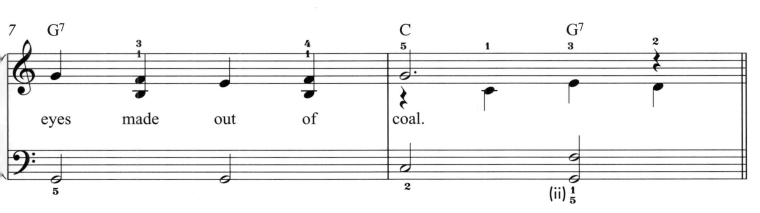

round.   Oh,   Frost -   y   the   snow - man   was a -

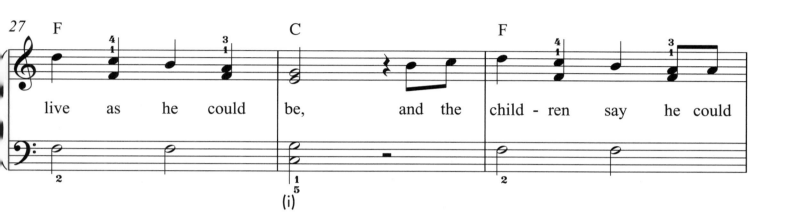

live   as   he   could   be,   and the   child - ren   say   he could

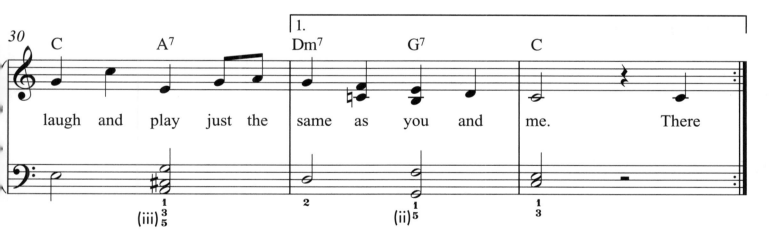

laugh and   play   just the   same   as   you   and   me.   There

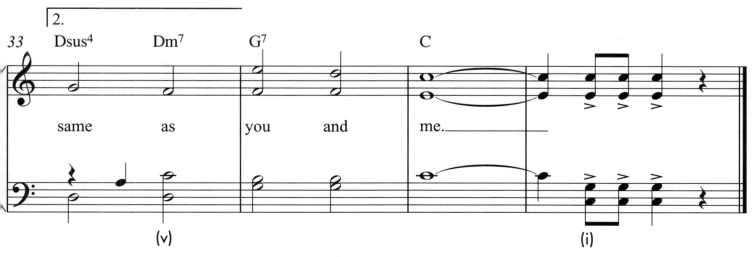

same   as   you   and   me.

In Dulci Jubilo

Traditional
English Words by R.L. Pearsall

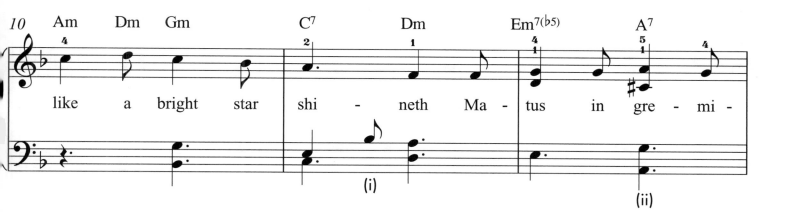

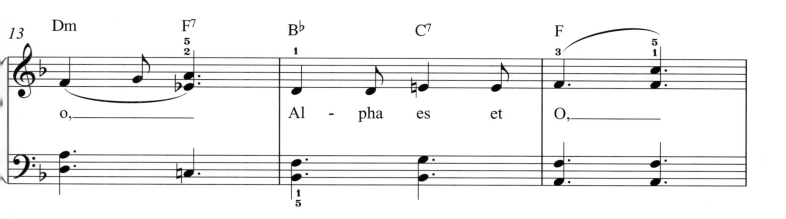

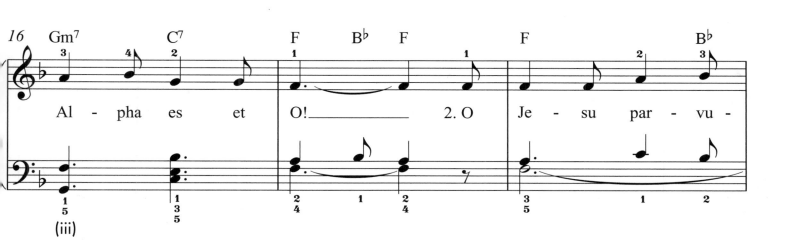

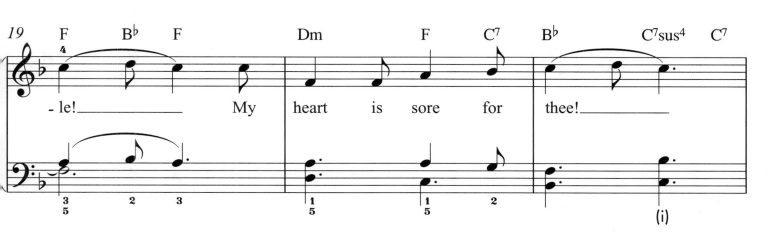

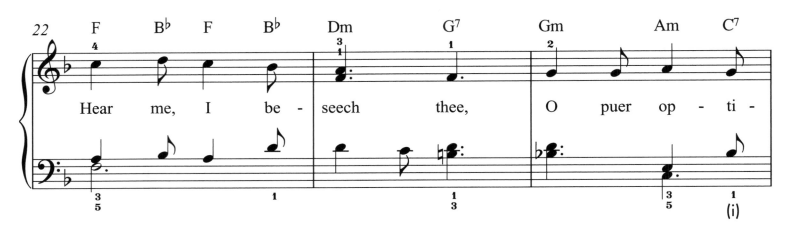

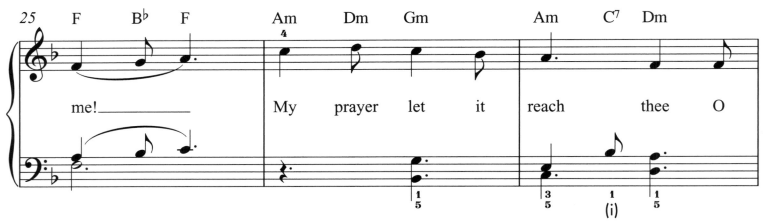

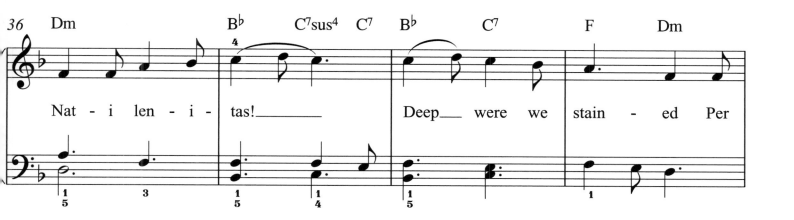

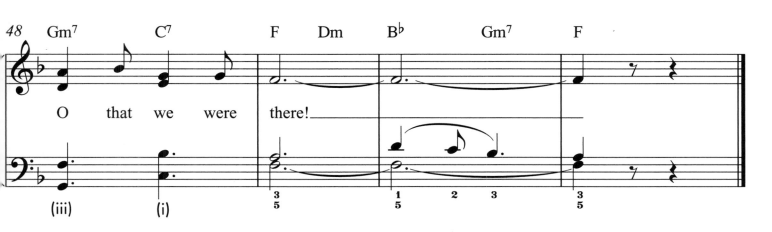

Jingle Bell Rock

Words & Music by Joseph Beal & James Boothe

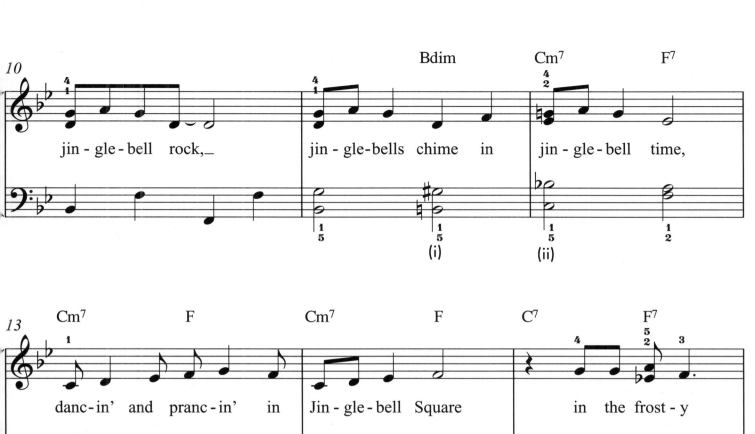

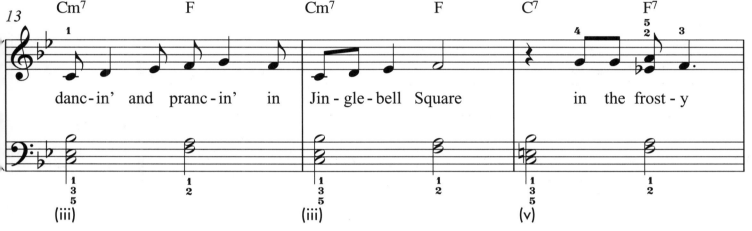

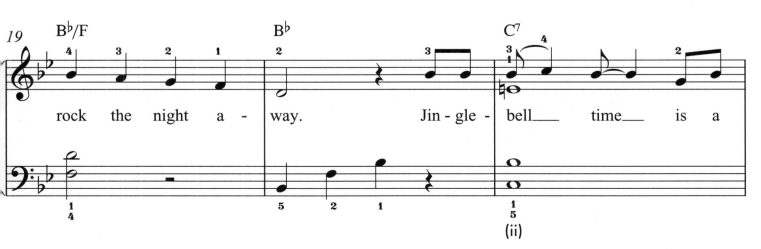

59

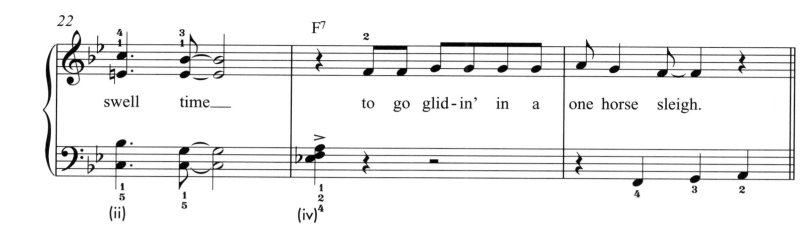

swell time___ to go glid-in' in a one horse sleigh.

Gid-dy-ap, jin-gle horse, pick up your feet, jin-gle a-round the clock.

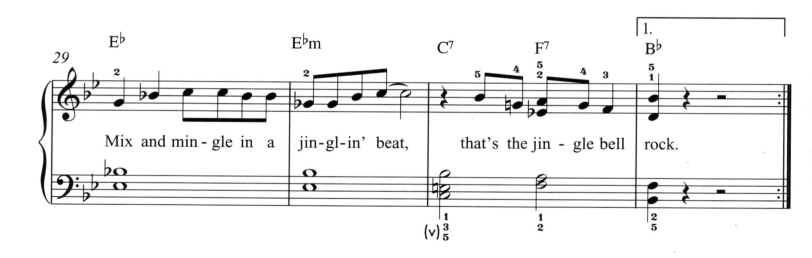

Mix and min-gle in a jin-gl-in' beat, that's the jin-gle bell rock.

that's the jin-gle bell, that's the jin-gle bell rock.___

Winter Wonderland

Words by Richard Smith
Music by Felix Bernard

Glossary Of Symbols & Terms

Key

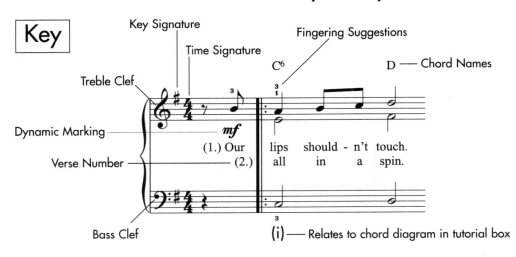

Key Signature
Time Signature
Fingering Suggestions
C⁶
D —— Chord Names
Treble Clef
Dynamic Marking
Verse Number
Bass Clef
(i) —— Relates to chord diagram in tutorial box

Each piece is accompanied by this box which highlights the *key signature*, as well as any *accidentals* in the order in which they appear in the music:

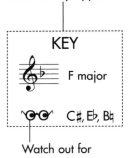

KEY

F major

C♯, E♭, B♮

Watch out for

Symbols

Tie — When two similar notes are tied together, the value of each note is added together. So, the value of the tied notes in this example is six crotchet beats.

Slur — A slur over a group of notes indicates that they should be played as a smooth phrase. N.B. A slur occurs above or below a series of *different* notes, while a tie is always placed next to similar notes (see above).

Dots above or below notes indicate they should be played *Staccato*, i.e. short and crisp.

This symbol indicates the notes should be played *Sforzando*, i.e. heavily accented.

p = piano (quiet)

mp = mezzopiano (moderately quiet)

pp = pianissimo (very quiet)

f = forte (loud)

mf = mezzoforte (moderately loud)

ff = fortissino (very loud)

R.H. = Right Hand   L.H. = Left Hand

= *diminuendo* (get quieter)

= *crescendo* (get louder)

⌢ = *pause* (note is held on for longer than its value)

= *start repeat*   = *end repeat*   8ᵛᵃ- - - - -┐ Indicates music to be played an octave higher than written.

(♩♩ = ♩♪) instead of playing straight quavers, they should be swung, i.e. lengthen the first note and shorten the second.

|1. On the *first* time of playing, follow this bar.

|2. On the *second* time of playing, follow this bar.

Terms

Andante = at a steady, walking pace

rit. = *ritenuto*, meaning to slow down gradually

rall. = *rallentando*, meaning to slow down gradually

a tempo = return to the original speed suggested at the start of a section

N.C. = no chord

⊕ **Coda** = indicates start of Coda section

To ⊕ Coda = jump to the start of the Coda section

D.S. al Coda = go back to the sign 𝄋 and play through to until you reach *To ⊕ Coda*

FINE = the end